Other books by Theodore Rubin:

JORDI
LISA AND DAVID
SWEET DADDY
IN THE LIFE
PLATZO AND THE
MEXICAN PONY RIDER

CAT

□ □

Theodore Isaac Rubin

BALLANTINE BOOKS   •   NEW YORK

For my sister Bibi

INTRODUCTION

This book is neither a novel nor a case history.

Its purpose is to communicate the feeling experiences of Frank, a man suffering from a schizophrenic catatonic reaction. Relating to the experiences involved in this condition may stimulate unconscious material, since there is much in Frank that exists in all of us. This may be threatening and anxiety-producing. It is not easy to allow oneself to become involved in deep pathology.

This book is not written in a conventional style, but I do not use the particular form whimsically. The style is bizarre, and the reader will at times be confused. However, Frank is confused too. He is suffering from a bizarre illness, and everything written in the book is as it is felt by Frank. With the exception of the notes at the end, and the description of the electro-convulsive treatment, all that is written is as perceived through his special hazy awareness.

There is no plot but rather a thread—a continuum. Every symbol has meaning on various levels. The book will probably have to be read slowly and several times to achieve maximum understanding of these symbols. Journeying through Frank's special world is difficult. The reader must allow himself to feel as well as to understand. I would like to quote my teacher, Dr. Nathan Freeman, who helped analytic candidates to understand better and to have feeling for the process of free association when he said: "The words are fine, but it is more important to listen to the music."

PREFACE

Frank, a 32-year-old man, has been
transferred from a general hospital to
a state hospital.

CAT

□ □

PART I

His arms went on doing their work. Since they were no longer part of him, he wasn't tired. They could go on and on holding up his hands. He thought, my hands my hands— the hands, the fingers. The arms, hands, fingers —they weren't his—not anymore. They just were, by themselves—and they did the job. The fingers pressed against his closed eyelids. The eyes were still his. The fingers held them in. He had a pact with the fingers. They promised him not to let his eyes fall out.

His arm was touched. He screamed—he didn't want to lose his eyeballs. He heard the voices. He heard CAT—the word cat. Then, what seemed a while afterward, he heard TONIC—the word tonic. He thought, cat tonic—cat tonic. Then he thought, health tonic. Then a voice said catotonic—putting an O between the words and putting the words together into one word. But it didn't make sense. Then it made sense. Cat O'Tonic, an Irish name—but he wasn't Irish. And his first name wasn't Cat. He kept hearing the voices. He heard the word EXCITEMENT. Another voice put the name and the new word together. He heard—Cat O'Tonic excitement.

Then he heard a voice screaming, and it screamed louder and louder. Now he heard the words—"I can't see, see, see, see, see, see. I can't see." He heard another voice say, "If he is so frantic about seeing, why doesn't he take his hands away from his eyes?" "Would it matter if he did?" said another voice.

Back, to go back; but black smoke, black smoke, the caving in, all of it coming down and blackness.

Waking but not seeing—brightness—bright, bright white brightness. Bright whiteness. The hospital and the wait, and the waiting some more, and waiting—waiting through miles and miles of white brightness. They never came. They stayed in the smoke, lost in the blackness. Nobody came. There was nobody. They were smoke—up, up, in blackness and smoke. The redness, then the coming of the redness—a brighter and brighter, deeper and deeper redness. The voices, farther and farther away—another world. Traveling away slowly, slowly disappearing—a word here, there, in the middle of the redness—out—out shut it out—no words—none—and black, then blue—the red to blue again—cold blue—cold sea icy blue. The whiteness gone, the bandages, gone, a new word here, there, a new world, new voices.

□□

"Go on, Sam—do your stuff, Sam."

"Come on, little eighter, eighter from De-catur—ah, shit, you lousy slob—an 8, I can't even make a lousy 8."

"Glad I finished sedation rounds, 10:30—off at noon tomorrow. Come on, Mike, coax the dice, boy, got money on you, boy."

"I don't ask much—just no craps—please, God—just don't crap out—for Christ sakes! I'm disgusted, boxcars—can ya imagine—all right dice—apologize now—apologize—shit —all right, I can make ten, I can make it—I made big dick before—big dick, big dick—hit damn it hit—who'll lay it—come on boy— I'll take—10 a 5—10 a 5—come on anybody —all right the hell with ya—big dick—55 the hard way, come on dice—you dirty son of a—"

"Okay, better break it up—resident be makin' night rounds soon."

"Little craps never hurt no one."

"Hurts me, man, hurts me now."

□□

Empty, empty-headed. But the tube, the tube was out. His penis hurt, the special smarting way it did when the tube was out. Now—if he was filled, he would not be empty. Empty—em pity—pity—pity—the em pity house. Safety—safe-e-ty. His father tried to teach him to spell it but couldn't, s-a-f-e-t-y, safety. Then the day of the party. 8—the eighth party. But it was the first. No money for the other 7, for the first 7. 8 years old—8—8 children—none came—none came. She forgot. She forgot. She just forgot. She never told them. She never told them to come. She forgot, just forgot. Sat there the whole eighth birthday—sat and sat and sat. The shade was changing from blue to pink. He had to hold it back. He started to stiffen again. He got stiffer as the pink changed to blue.

But the forgetting, her forgetting came back. The days he came from school—6—he was 6—6 point 5—6 and a half—6 decimal point 5. No lunch—and again and again no lunch—no lunch—no lunch—a hamburger she said—a hamburger—go to the store—here's a quarter a hamburger—ate it alone in the drugstore—a chopped—a chopped-up meatball.

CAT

Hear the raindrops rolling down the window glass. Raindrops turning red blood, blood red. He got stiffer and stiffer as the empty flatness came back.

"Poor guy—wonder if he's thinking."

"What they goin' to do with him?"

"E. C. T. I guess. God, what he's been through. Enough to make you crazy."

□□

CAT

Pearls and divers—the red pony.

Jack London—The South Seas—Jerry of the Islands. The Wild North Country—The Case of the Sleepy Bride.

☐☐

He kept his eyes glued to the wall that wasn't there. It wasn't a picture. It was happening—happening again right there.

The sand stretched endlessly in all directions and it was a windless time. There were little gulleys here and there, and ripples filled with clouded shadows and sun. He saw him treading softly on the sand, a pinpoint on the wide expanse. Then, as if by magic, he—Frank—felt his own bare feet against the warm and cool spots. Grains of sand trickled between his toes. He saw his tracks now, a small chain of footprints in the center of the sanded vastness. And he looked closely and knew that his feet had flattened a few of the countless ripples. He shuddered. The sky grew black and it started to rain. As the sand turned to mud, he thrashed back and forth, moaning softly. Then there was a voice in the middle of it. "Hot," it said, "he's very hot, burning up—will go into exhaust." Now he felt a coldness above his eyes. Some water from the compress dripped down his face. The ocean pounded the beach again. He lay back, relieving the restraints of their job. He closed his eyes and the sand came back to view. Only it was sunny again and near the ocean—a huge white beach. He wasn't part of the scene, just somebody outside looking in; looking at the waves and listening to the booming surf. Some seagulls flew into the scene, diving in and out of the shallow water scooping up beakfuls of jumping sand eels. A large group of sandpipers scurried by, leaving little herringbone tracks in their wake. A man appeared, walking along in ankle-deep water, picking up odd shells and stones here and there. Then a group of terns flew by, and the man turned and stared at him. Now he recognized him. It was himself. A shrill, high voice exploded in his head. At first he couldn't hear the words. Then they came through crystal clear, each word like an icicle. When he put the icicles together, they clanged out loud and sharp—You had to get into the scene, couldn't you stay out Frank? stay out Frank—stay out! He thrashed about again as the nurse bathed his hot, flushed face with ice water.

□□

CAT

Swimming along, alone in a dark-blue pool —and a glimmer of gold—a shimmering, glimmering gold—the fish.

Cover the bowl—cover it—cover it. Yes she had said but no—on the floor still jumping on the hard red floor. Bruised but swimming— swimming to jump again—the cover—put it on—but no—the jumping fish on the floor —dried and hard and dull and dead and all the pushing and salting and crying—but the fish curled dry—dry dead. The spoon, the silver spoon and the golden fish—into the bowl —the same bowl as the baby guppy fish— poured down—she flushed and all out to the sewer and back to the sea—to a dark-blue pool —tossed here and there by the water—the life-giving sea giving life again—to and fro—swimming along—alone with the baby guppies— no, alone—alone and dead.

"He looks okay."

"Very pale."

"They all like that—he's okay."

Swimming, swimming—bloodless, pale—the golden glimmering close and closer. Mouth open and close—open and close—and closer and closer. Chopped up. Angry, teeth angry

13

—little pieces—here and there—an arm—a leg—a head—floating apart—more water between — separate — separate — pieces — apart. NO.

"Listen to 'im yell. Told you—stay the hell away—now he's getting excited."

The screaming voice from the distance—the screaming voice—other sounds close by, but far away.

Together—moving closer together—less distance and water between the parts. The head on the neck on the torso. The arms and legs —and the eyes—the eyes. In—back again—in, into the head. The golden glimmer gone.

□□

"Okay, put the needle on."

"A 22?"

"No, I like a short 20 intramuscular."

"I'll have to get one."

"I'll wait."

The paramecium stalks its prey and the amoeba slithers along.

"Here you are, doctor."

"Thanks. I'm glad this guy has good veins. There we go. No, that's too fast."

"Okay?"

"That's better—let these infusions drip slowly."

"Okay."

"Better tape it better than that."

A giant ciliated paramecium.

"Not likely that he'll move."

A giant amoeba.

"Can't tell."

"This better?"

"Too good. You'll cut off his circulation."

Pseudopods.

"How's this?"

Pseudociliatedparamoebicpods.

"Fine, let's go."

□□

Blood money—blood money—I sweat blood for it—sweat blood—sweat and blood.

Ma—your face—beads of blood—salted blood running down your face—pools and pools of blood—and money—dollars and dollars and dollars soaking in the pools—red red pools—the redness.

"He's tossing again—get Miss Riley give him a shot."

"Okay, Sam."

Pools, pools of oil black thick murky oil. Black—black.

"Wait, Jack—he's calming down."

"Stiffening up again?"

"Yeah—stiffening up."

□□

Shaking but at least alive—temp 104—burning up—he said burning up. She sponged and cared—she cared—mom—cared—the bed tucked in—the radio playing—and now a mountain of lifeless lumped-up flesh—that doesn't quiver—that's like a rock falling in space and falling, no feeling and falling—and no place to go. Free fall—free to fall—fall from feeling, through a black void—an emptiness, falling in an emptiness—without a star to light the way—without a tie.

"No change here."

"Okay, wait a minute—let me jot it down in my progress notes."

Falling—falling—all the way—through miles and miles of space—space is endless—and at the endlessness there's more endless, endless space. A rock—a heavy, empty rock—a rock—free fall—no interference—none at all—no friction—no contact—no warmth—no heat—cold—a cold fall.

□□

"You know something, Jack?"

"Yeah?"

"Sometimes, I get sick."

"What you sick about?"

"Look at this guy—or that one there—or any of these guys. Being attendants, it's all right, but they get you down."

"They're sick people, pal—there but for the love of God goes me or you."

"I got enough problems—cut the religion, man."

"So stop bitchin'."

"Not bitchin', but these guys lyin' here, poor buggers—like vegetables—gets a guy down."

"Some of them walk."

"Yeah, the walkin' dead."

"Let's go, boy, plenty to do upstairs."

□□

Saved up, saved up. Here are four roses—for you, mom, four roses. Put them in the kitchen—remember, she says—remember, remember to buy 'em for me when I'm dead—don't need them now. When dead—run down, she says—run down—get me cigarettes—cigarettes. Smoke—fill her up with smoke—smoke, a hazy blue smoke—from a red-hot fire—keep it back. The blue haze turning red—down—keep it down—yell. The lump sitting there in the chest. Can't yell. Cigarettes bad for the chest. Here, pop, here. I bought it for you, pa—thirty-five cents, with the tobacco, a cigarette-making machine, pop. You'll always have them, pop. Gee, he says. Gee, Frank, that's awfully nice. Your thinking of me this way. This is the nicest present I ever got, Frank—the best. Tears, pop tears—why tears? Happy, Frank, happy. Tears, tears—tears changed the red smoke to blue and made it cool again—cool.

"This guy get his feeding yet?"

"Yeah—just a while ago."

The rug—the time the rug came—rug time. Sara danced. A life in her—a death in Frank.

CAT

Water bubbling up and down, over many little rocks. A stagnant pool, deep and dark, a dead mosquito on the top.

On the bus going home again and there is
Mr. O'Connor, Harold's father. Hello, and
Mr. O'Connor says hello in a heavy Irish
brogue asking how the folks are doing. Feeling
a little nauseous with the bus bumping and
lurching and wondering why Harold is skinny
when his father is so fat. The bus is on the
Crossbay Bridge now and suddenly it feels like
a dream. It feels like it because dreaming it he
knows that he hadn't seen the bay or any
water for such a long time. But he stiffens and
stops thinking because he doesn't want to stop
dreaming, and with a little effort goes back to
the dream. Though he still dreams, an awake
dream, the thinking causes a shift of scene. It
was nighttime, July. He and Harold were 13
years old. It was the year before Hal moved
away. He was in the O'Connor kitchen; Harold's mother was serving a stew. It smelled
awfully good. Then she asked them to run
over to Hogan's Bar for a container of beer.
He watched the bartender fill the tall 2-quart
container. It was a hot night and the beer
looked so good, the foam nice and thick.
When they got back the family was seated at
the large round table. There were Hal's father

and mother, his two sisters, Mary 18 and Anne 15. Frank ate with them as he had so often done. The stew was delicious. It was very hot in the room and the stew made everybody even hotter, but that just made the cold beer even better, and then the beer made the stew still better. It was a pleasure cycle all around.

And now dead. When did he die? when?

☐☐

"Observe the patient, gentlemen. The picture is a classic one. Note the rigidity of the entire body, including the facies. Almost like a decerebrated cat."

Cat again—cat—why cat why?

"Note the waxy flexibility. At first there was so much rigidity. It was almost impossible to move his hands from his eyes. Do you hear me, Frank? What is it that you didn't want to see? Was it the fire, Frank?"

The fire—fire—red. There it was again, the redness—cool cool green blue cool keep it cool cool. There was a huge fire. He saw it now. He saw it all again. But this time there was no red feeling in him. He kept it down. He kept the red down and out—out—out of him. But the fire blazed on. The building began to crumble—all he could see through the red haze was the white-hot outlines of it. A man ran out—he just made it. But they were in there—the kids—the kids—Frank, go back —go back. The voice in his head screamed go back—go back, Frank. The smoke burned his eyes. They would melt. They would fall out. He held them, he held them tightly.

"Frank, you heard me. You're holding your

eyes again." Then the voice touched his hands. The red welled up in him. He couldn't hold it back. He screamed wildly. He heard the voice screaming—he couldn't stop now.

"He's going into an excitement again. Fortunately he is in restraint. Most destructive, these catatonic excitements."

Through it all, the name again—the name again Cat—Cat O'Tonic.

□□

The monkey landed on the back of the chair and for a while just sat there screeching. Then, noticing its shadow, it jumped off and chased it along the wall and out of the room.

He saw himself sitting on the chair and looking around. Then he realized there was no shadow on the wall. He got up and ran forward, then backward, then up and down, but there was still no shadow. He ran to the full-length mirror. There was no reflection, no reflection of himself. The mirror reflected the bed, the chair, the window, but not himself. Then he saw the monkey in the mirror. It looked at him very solemnly. Then it pointed at him from the mirror and began to laugh hysterically in a high screeching voice.

"Feed him yet?"

"About an hour ago."

He lay back and the incident was there again. The crowd kept walking on so that they were almost a block away now. He said nothing to her. Then they sat down on the bus bench. It was enclosed in a cement shelter, which gave him the feeling of being alone with her in a little house.

She stood up for a second to straighten her sweater. He saw his chance. He quickly stretched out his arm along the back of the bench, hoping to let it fall on her shoulder when she sat down again. Then she sat next to him. But he kept his arm stiff and just couldn't bring it to her shoulder. He hated himself— and hated her—not really—and yet he'd do it, he'd do it, but what if she laughed? He never held a girl before. He might look ridiculous— awkward—angry. He, Frank, awkward—he just couldn't take the chance. But she smelled so good. He stood up. His arm hurt. Without thinking, blurting out, all you dames ever think about are clothes! He didn't know why he said it. But the tension was gone—and he thought, the hell with her! Burt, hey, Burt, let's play some Ping-Pong. He walked toward the crowd and she followed.

The hole in his chest whenever he thought about it. Something had been missed, something never to be had again. The hole in his chest. He felt it again, but now it went right down through the bed to the floor. Deep as to the ocean floor.

Who is Frank? Frank is nobody. I am Frank —I am nobody.

Nobody walked with her—nobody talked to her.

She walked and talked with nobody.

But she, Sara, made nobody somebody.

She said, kiss me, kiss me, Frank—and the fright—the fright to do it right. Couldn't move, stiff—stiff—and then she kissed nobody lightly on nobody's lips.

She kisses nobody—nobody becomes somebody, somebody became Frank.

Now—no Sara—no Frank—nobody—none.

CAT

A head—an empty head—a corroded brain—
an empty shell— a dark, empty shell of a skull
—empty space—empty but crowded—crowds
and crowds—things—memories—memories—
floating around by themselves—eyes turned
in, inside out—looking at them—bumping
here, there—against the skull—hitting each
other—faces and places—and voices and things
—designs—designs and all the time—the in-
side-out eyes, looking, looking—seeing all and
feeling not at all. Just nothing.

Biology, Sara, I'm finally a biology teacher.
Biology—what is it? What is biology—what
—necrology—what is necrology—an empty
head, an empty heart, an empty body—only
knows emptiness.

□□

They were on the boardwalk facing the ocean. The waves were high and strong. There were many whitecaps. The beach was desolate. They clung to each other and felt that they were alone in a wild place by the sea. It was difficult to feel that the great city of New York was only fifteen miles away.

They walked down to the ocean, faced the surf and kissed. Her lipstick tasted good mixed with the salt of the air. After a while, they walked parallel to the ocean, hand in hand, cold but happy.

"Young man, Amytal may bring him out and may not. In any case, aside from dramatic effect, it would serve no purpose. Its results at best would only be temporary and I feel may traumatize the patient. ECT can bring him out and maybe keep him out awhile."

□ □

"Poor fella, poor fella. Hope this gives you some relief."

"He's not suffering—he's way off—helpless but painless."

"He's suffering—I think he's suffering awfully—look at his face—so pale—drawn."

"Oh, what do you— Quiet, here comes Dr. Finch."

"Hello, Frank. We're going to give you your first treatment today, Frank. We won't hurt you. We want to help you."

He lay flat on his back. He didn't care about the two pillows under his hips or the band around his forehead or the contact jelly on his skin.

"Put the electrodes under the band."

The electrodes—the wires—so this was it finally—to be burned up—a burning—an electrode—electrical—wired up burning. He stiffened and waited to go up in smoke—black smoke.

He didn't resist. It didn't occur to him to resist. He felt the cloth-wrapped tongue depressor between his teeth but just let it rest—hardly biting on it at all. He waited for the fire—stiff—stiff—stiffer—hard—as hard as a rock—but burn—burn. Suddenly there was a void—a coldness—emptiness—a nothingness. His body contracted into a spasm. His toes stretched out and toward each other. His eyes went up into his head and his closed eyelids twitched rapidly. All of his muscles contracted as part of the induced epileptic seizure. His body leaped against the nurses' hands. Almost simultaneously he inhaled, making a terribly deep guttural sound as air forced its way through the now contracted glottis. He remained convulsed, his teeth clamped on the tongue depressor as white spittle dribbled down his chin. His face became bluer, bluer, dark and purple. He didn't breathe. Then finally there was a sharp intake of air. His face became rosy again. His muscles relaxed. The nurses let go of his body, which no longer strained against their hands.

Consciousness again—and confusion—a muddling with it—and then the sinking into a deep sleep—the first in a long, long time.

□ □

CAT

I was very young, seems like long ago but it is now and yet then. He had brought a new deck of cards from uncle Will's store to the corner gang. They played poker—and the new cards felt good in his hands. He keeps winning. Suddenly Tim Mahoney, a very wiry, foxy-looking boy, grabs the deck and runs away. I chase him—and each time nearly catch him, but just miss. Tim takes a card—I could see it —the ace of spades—and slowly starts to tear it down the middle. I scream, but can't catch him. The other players sit as an audience and watch. The ace is nearly ripped in half now. Mahoney runs a little distance and taunts me. He is making funny faces at me. He throws the pack of cards up in the air and runs over to me and slaps me. I hit back, but Tim is too fast. He hit Frank again and again, but ducked out of reach each time I lunged forward. Frank's face was a bloody mess now. I could hardly see. I heard myself yelling—Mahoney —weasel—little weasel. I don't yell at all.

□ □

He walked into Hector's on Broadway, figuring he'd get some meat loaf and a cup of coffee for lunch.

Walking to a table with his tray he saw her —recognized her at once. The sharp feeling caught in his chest—it was something he hadn't felt in years. With it came a great wave of gladness, and a fright too. He was a teenager again, idolizing her, shy, happy, and there was the memory of a failure—and the feeling of weakness and with it all an uneasiness, almost a premonition of danger—a wave of fear. But they talked and talked and life filled him. He almost danced through the streets to the subway. And they married and now dead— he was dead.

"Oh, yes indeed, in general hospitals we see many many psychotic depressions, manic reactions, even catatonic excitements—but here and there a catatonic stupor like this one turns up too, and then we ship them over to this place."

The rain beat down, gently bending the grass against the earth, and there were little puddles here and there. Then he noticed a tiny frog blinking at him through the grass. As he walked past her, she winked at him, first one eye, then the other. He wondered whether she was a frog or a toad, and finally decided she was a flirt—just a flirty little frog. The rain felt cool against his skin, even soothing; and the green grass smelled fresh and light. He walked on, and soon came to a huge stack of hay. He climbed to the top of it and then lay flat on his back. The sun came out and the hay smelled strong but pleasant. Then he heard the whistling, sat up and looked toward the green grass. As the girl came close he waved and yelled to her, and she waved back. He ran down the haystack and they rushed toward each other. He heard her say, Frank, Frank, I've found you, I found you.

"Hey, Sam, you know, he actually looks at peace with himself."

"Good."

Hear the rain come down cats and dogs, dogs and cats.

The kitten rubs itself against the wall. It arches its back and seems to become thin and tall. Then it crouches down and tries to shrink itself into a little ball. But it is getting more and more lethargic. It doesn't play anymore and it stops eating.

Frank watches the wall, the wall that isn't there. Maybe it needs cat tonic. Then he sees his father again. He picks up the shivering kitten. He says that it is sick. He will take it to the animal doctor and bring it back.

Frank hears the crash. His father's car is in pieces all over the street. His father is gone and he will never bring the kitten back.

A redness in him wells up. He stiffens to keep it back. The hard lump in his chest gets harder. His head feels like lead—heavier, heavy as a statue. He lies still. The redness is turning to pink now and green and misty blue. The kitten is gone.

□□

CAT

The crowd, the crowd, people—sharks.

The sharks swayed in time to the music. You could hardly notice them dancing. They just swayed up and back, entranced by the beat. She was suddenly there in the middle of it all. They came to life and quickly made room in the center for her to do her stuff. She was dressed in a one-piece, skin-tight leotard. She did a modern dance with many stiff deep-knee bands and spectacular leaps. When she stopped she didn't bow. Instead, she jerked her head up and thrust her chin out, in a proud, defiant manner. The crowd cheered and clapped wildly. And then they began to chant over and over again: Bravo—Sara—Bravo, Bravo, Bravo Sara. She felt happy, high, exhilarated, but continued to keep herself proud and aloof, looking at the adoring crowd with boredom and detachment.

Then her eyes wandered for a moment and caught sight of her breasts. They were huge, long, hard and pointed, and had come through the tight garment she wore. Then she realized that their applause was not for her dancing at all. She covered her bosom with her hands and tried to run and melt into the crowd. But

they formed a solid wall resisting each of her
efforts and pushing her back to the center of
the floor. Then she heard somebody whisper,
what a dish—and she screamed.

"What is he screaming about?"

"Beats me."

He was young again—the people—Sara. How come you have a mustache?

Her sun-tanned face immediately heated into a deep crimson. She turned her head away, trying to avoid the four pairs of eyes now focused on her upper lip. She kept her head stiff, not making a sound or a move. She even breathed quietly, maybe feeling that this would help her to meld into her surroundings. This would make the remark fade away too. Later, after it was gone, maybe she could come back and be herself again. But her heart gave her away to herself. He knew it was her heart, but he could feel it too. It beat wildly, and the loud feeling of it kept her and him aware of herself. And so she must have felt the word— mustache—the hair on her upper lip, and their eyes. Then the giant sob welled up in her, and she ran into the bungalow and threw herself on the bed. He wanted to tell her that he felt the pain too. But, no—didn't know how. No—no—the chance to help and no.

□□

CAT

You gotta keep clean, Frank, you gotta keep clean, always clean—inside out, Frank—inside and out. If nothing else—remember—you'll always remember your mother kept you clean. Clean thoughts—actions—clothes—a clean boy—it counts—it shows—people will like you.

Clean—clean—clean white bones—picked clean—dry—bleached, white—ammonia white —white shirt smelling of ether—you smell, boy—smell. Tell your mother to wash the ammonia out—rash, boy—you've got a rash.

□ □

"Everything okay, Sam?"

"All quiet, Miss Riley."

Let's go to that outdoor hamburger place—where? You know, on Flatbush Avenue near Avenue U—okay. Driving along silently. What's amatter, Frank? Something eating you? Feeling panicky, trying to smile—but lips that won't obey. Instead, a lower lip that quivers. As if control of the muscles of the face is lost. Frank, what gives? I, I, well, I don't know—I'm tired. I guess. Been working hard. She smiles. Sara smiles.

"Where's the headband?"
"Here, doctor."
"Ready?"
"I gottim."
"Me too."
"Okay, here goes."

CAT

The party—the time of the party—the children and Sara—a regular birthday party—a kid surprise party for a grown man. But Sara and the kids and blowing out the candles and the four of us—our four family—laughing and clapping—the best party—the only party—just for me. Did it happen—did it happen—Sara and the kids—they happened—they happened—an empty world—a dead world—a dead world—a world of flatness and deadness—world of nothing happening—world of haplessness.

CAT

Burn me up—burn me up again—the wires—the electricity—fry me—burn—burn.

"This is your fifth treatment, Frank; 7 to go. Hold him now!"

Looser looser—soft, softer—safe—safer—safety—empty—empty—pity—pity house—house of pity. Sara, Sara—me, Sara and me and the kids. No hamburgers—no chopped-up meatballs—Sara—mine—mine—mine.

They walk on the beach kicking up little mounds of sand here and there. The water rolls in gently. Linda and Billy are up ahead. The bonfire on the beach—the children walk into it—into the red glow. Sara runs after them—they are in the middle of it now. He coaxes the ocean—please—please—not so calm—not so stiff—roll in—roll in. It rolls—the sea rolls up to the edge of the flames—no further—no further—the sea is not magic—the sea is the sea—is the sea—see see the man—alone—a hamburger again at the counter—the drugstore counter.

□□

Hey, look at those hands—Billy—gotta wash them—can't eat with dirty hands—germs.

Leave him, Sara—leave him be—they're not bad.

But Frank—

They're okay, Sara—I know all about the germ theory. I say sit, Billy. Eat your supper.

What's the matter, Frank?

Don't know—I don't know.

Hard day?

Guess so. Hard day.

A cold, hard day—stretched out—from morning to nighting.

□□

The house, remember there it is. It's there again. The down payment—contract—closing —taking possession—the Cokes and Sara making the sandwiches—and painting and wall-papering—our house—snowflakes, outside— our world. After work—the house—cozy— painting it, stopping, a Coke—a bite to eat. Then the moving, moving in. No furniture, but full, full of us—a house; the first time, a house.

"How are you, Frank?"

The house—like a boat—floating along— a boat on an ocean—complete.

"Frank!"

A boat—a strong, closed, complete boat.

"All right—let's go, Miss Riley."

"Yes, doctor."

Complete—the outside, the storm. But a boat, fortified, with all—a house boat—moving—moving on.

□□

She's your mother, Frank. We will go to the funeral.

Yes, Sara, we will go to her funeral.

"Tell 'em to turn up the heat."

"Okay, Sam."

□□

"There is no such thing as a typical reaction of any kind. Just as we are all a mixture of many things, a reaction is likewise a mixture of many things. Now, most of the people on this ward have been diagnosed as schizophrenic reactions—catatonic type. However, you may well find elements of all the other schizophrenic types—hebephrenia, paranoia—and, of course, depression, and even evidence of raw anxiety. But in most of these people—the predominant presenting symptoms—the stupors, the excitements, the autism, the bodily rigidity, the waxy flexibility, and, of course, the inability to handle anger as well as the rest of the lifelong personality dynamic processes—suffice to substantiate the diagnosis of catatonia. But, of course, there may well be hallucinatory and delusional phenomena as well as paranoid ideation, and the characteristics of the other psychotic reactions as well as neurotic characteristics too. Remember, there are people who feel that schizophrenia is actually an illness consisting of several steps—catatonia being an early step in the progression, which, unless arrested, goes on to paranoia, the end phase. This theory is, of course, opposed to the one that sees each schizophrenic reaction as a separate diagnostic entity."

"Can any of these people understand us, sir?"

"Some can hear us and may understand us —and that's why we will continue our discussion of individual cases upstairs. Thank you for having us in, Miss Riley."

"You're most welcome, Dr. Franz."

"Good-bye."

"Good-bye."

"Say, who are all these people, Miss Riley?"

"That's Dr. Franz—professor at the medical school—and his students. Comes here every so often."

"Oh, I see—gee, he could sure talk."

"I guess that's his job, Jack."

□□

Frank—do you hear me, Frank?

I hear you—I hear you.

You have ears, Frank?

I don't know—but I hear you.

You dig me, Frank? You dig me?

Dig—digging out of a big deep hole.

Hole—whole what?

A big deep hole. Cover him with sand, more sand. My chest hurts. Can't breathe. Leave him, leave him—uncover him—uncover him —brush the sand away.

Frank, Frank, Frank.

Leave me, leave me, whoever you are—leave me—go—go—go.

Frank

Go

Frank

Go

Gone—no voice—quiet again and stiff.

□ □

PART II

Talk to me, talk, Frank, talk—don't go on being angry, Frank. Talk, Frank, talk. Get it over, Frank, get it over—yell at me, hit me, anything—but don't sulk this way—I can't take it.

All right, Frank, I'm going to kiss you—be angry—but I'm going to kiss you—I'm going to melt your stubbornness, Frank—I'm going to melt that pride. You told me once, remember? You said pay no attention, you said you can't make the first move—Frank, I'm making it—I am—I love you so much, Frank.

Sara, melt me—melt me—Sara, melt me— Oh Sara, melt me—now Sara, Sara—Sara.

Frank, Frank, Frank, FRANK, FRANK.

I hear you, Sara, I hear you—I hear you— say more, more, Sara, more.

"Going into an excitement again—look at him thrash."

"Get Miss Riley—she'll give him a shot."

Frank, Frank, FRANK, FRANK—melt, melt—melt.

I heard you, Sara—I heard you, Sara—I heard you.

"He's not excited—look—calm as you please."

"Gee, sure looked it a minute ago, Miss Riley." □□

There was no life in him. There had been a leak, a big leak. When they put the pipe into him, the life leaked out.

His body thrashed against the restraints. He marveled at it. The life had leaked out but the body, his body, seemed to be alive. His body was alive. He was dead.

Then he got the new idea. He opened his mouth. He left it open. He waited and waited. But the voice in the next bed didn't understand. His mouth stayed open for a time—a long, long time. He heard a new voice say, "Talk. Frank, go ahead, you're about to—say it, Frank, say it." The man didn't understand. He wanted the man to breathe life into his mouth. But the voice just said, "What is it— what, Frank?" And finally the voice faded away.

□□

"This cookie is lost."

"What do you mean, lost?"

"Lost is lost—I mean lost—*finito*."

"You can't tell—the jolts may straighten him out."

"Jolts?"

"Jolts, jolts—some electricity, boy."

"You mean shock."

"Yeah man, shock treatments."

"I still say lost, poor bugger."

Lost—bugs—shopping in the crowds—gone —she's gone—and I'm alone—in the big crowd. Alone—the policeman—and home. Where were you, Frankie? Where the devil you disappear to? Home, you left me and went home. Was tired—knew you'd be all right, Frankie. You're a big boy now. After all, you're almost 8—you know your way home—the crowds—lost in the big crowd.

"Come on, boy, hurry up—got upstairs to do yet."

"Okay, 'stead of standing watching—help me finish—sweep up."

A crowd of voices—hard, sharp, pointy voices. Stick here, stick there—lost in a crowd of voices.

□□

"Superimpose trauma on a lifetime of trauma—and such a cruel trauma—such a loss. Sit with him, sit with him, Dr. Green—with the ECT—sit—just be there."

Traumer—baumer, EasyT—Easy Tea—Green—cool green—Sit green—Green sit.

"This is Dr. Green, Frank—Dr. Green will be your doctor. He will try to help you and will be with you. You don't have to do anything, Frank. But when you want to talk, Dr. Green—Green will be here—he's here to help you. Good luck, Frank."

Luck, luck—much—much—much—much—much—much—muck—muck muck.

"I'm going to sit here with you, Frank, twice a day, every day for at least 45 minutes each session. I'll be here at 10 in the morning and 3 in the afternoon. Today is Monday. I won't be here this Sunday. Some Sundays I will be here. I'm not going to read, write or do anything except to be with you. I know that you know I'm here. When you're ready to, we will talk together."

10—3—3—10—there were 10 men on the 3 dead men's chests—on a dead man's chest—10.

□□

"Sam, you got a cigarette?"

Can't bet.

"Yeah—but smoke in the toilet."

Just a small bet, Frank.

"Okay."

I never bet—never bet—never let—never bet—never—sits there like a mass of flesh—never, never bet.

□□

"Look at that leak—plop—plop—ploppin' away."

Plop—clop—chop—cop—a cop is a solid thing to be—cops and robbers—an automatic —6-shooter.

"Maintenance coming over?"

· "I called him."

Plop—giddy youp—pop—the pony—is it hard for him to pull 6 kids? Shetlands are strong—small but strong.

Plop—flop.

□□

"Well healed—plenty though—sure been through plenty."

"Eyes."

"I know."

"If only someone—isn't there? I mean anyone?"

"Green."

"Yes, but."

"But, let's go."

Go—go—and gone—green—green—a carpet of green and no one on it—no one dancing. Stretching off into space—space and rockets, Rockettes—kick—left right—kick—kick—precise—even like a machine. Yes, uncle Will, like a machine. Waiting on line. Radio City—Little Minister—the Roxy—the candy smell. The movie—Christmas rich smell—uncle Will's damp coat smell. A father to you, I'll be—and the Rockettes—kick in line—like one person. Uncle Will and home—first Hector's —meat loaf—gravy—potatoes—macaroni— light and bright—and talking, people talking. So quiet, Frank—so quiet. Quiet uncle Will —quiet. Not the bus—Frank—the train— fun over the trestle—fun—back over the water —the lighted train—to the dark rooms—the 3 rooms to sleep in—through the winter over the bridge—the summer resort in the winter—in the dark, cold frozen, stiff winter—a ghost town quiet—silent.

"It's me, Frank, I've come for our hour. It's warm out, Frank. There's the smell of spring in the air."

Spring—warm—the ghost voice is warm— the town over the trestle—the ghost town— painted and waiting—for the summer—the buses and trains over the trestle—over the bridges—connected—and living again.

CAT

"Okay, hold him."

"Hold it, doctor—gag slipped."

Gag like a rag—treatment of a rag by electricity.

"Okay, doc—shoot."

Shot.

□□

The smell—the smell—a Christmas tree—tinsel—steam heat smell.

"Don't bother there, boy. Tube fed—he wants no soup, boy."

"Okay. One less to feed."

Soup, the cold boardwalk—how cold it could get and then he ate the hot soup—clam chowder and the steam heat smell. The ocean, the cold, cold ocean—stretching deep—deep and stretching—no end—in the middle—a blob —just a blob—in the middle—a blob in the middle of it—part of it—a blob bobbing up and down—then down and gone. A clam in the chowder—a piece of clam—lifeless—away —part of the sea.

"Well, Merry Christmas, fellows—Merry Christmas to all of you—you too, over there, boy—even if you can't hear me, Merry Christmas, fella."

"Come on, boy—got another ward to feed."

"Okay, I'm comin'."

Christmas, the little globe, the little glass ball on her dresser. Full of snowflakes and a little tree. Upside down and the flakes flurry all about—all about. The world is full of flakes of snow—and the tree—the tree of Christmas

—a cold dead quiet lonely snow globe world
—quiet, safe, warm, warm soup—a glob—but
too big for the globe—her snowy globe world
filled with Christmas and the tinsel steam heat
smell.

□□

"Come on, boy. I'm gonna wash you up, man—nice and clean. Come on, fella—gonna change your jamas and sheets—nice and clean. Make you feel nice, boy—fresh, clean—now just gonna turn you a bit, Frankie boy."

Fingers cool against a body dead. Slim hands and fingers against a body alive. 2 hands intertwined, moving and alive, on a sun-swept beach—a bright, light beach—no smoke in the air.

The sun and sea seen together, see. Scene to view, a view with eyes anew. New eyes. Red, oh so red.

"Loosen up, boy, let me get this sleeve on. That's it. Now you look nice, Frankie fella. Be good now, see you later."

See good—be good—good—later—later, a place, a person—thing or what? A time—a time—later, a time. Later, a later time.

"How about it, Sam, how about it?"

"No, not me. Count me out, boy."

"Oh, come on, Sam—a little craps won't hurt no one."

"Not me, boy—not me."

"Why not, Sam?"

"Jack, it ain't right—it just ain't right."

"Oh, Sam—no one'll get hurt."

"Jack, we're supposed to be on duty."

"Can be on duty and shoot a little crap—nothing ever happens around here anyway."

"You'd be surprised."

"Well, we're just gonna be in the toilet, man. We'll hear anything happens on the ward."

"No dice, Jack."

"Oh, shit, man."

"Look, pal, I just got no money—get me—no mazola—no gelt—no bread—no dough."

"That's different—I dig you, boy."

Dig—dig—dig—crap. Mahoney don't crap around.

□□

"Did you get it out?"

"Out and gone."

"Hurt?"

"No—gave me Novocain."

Nova Cain—new Cain—a new devil spreading and numbing—killing—and deading.

"Boy, can't neglect your teeth."

"First one I ever lost."

"Okay man—I'm gonna skidoo."

Perdu—perdu—perdu.

□□

"Boy, Sam, I got some heartburn, man."

"Too much party last P.M., Jack boy?"

Burn, burn—my heart burns—a ball of fire in my chest. A flame burning in the middle of me—charring, charring—charring. All in the wake is charred and crumbling—dead white ash.

"What a broad, man, what a broad."

The day the boardwalk burned down—the fire engines, no boardwalk left, pieces of wood here and there, hanging down to the beach, the smell of smoke and charred blackness for weeks and weak. The day Tony caught the weak fish. The fish seemed strong.

"What a dish—a real beautiful broad."

Broad, broad—Sara—the walks on the broad boardwalk.

"Nice."

"Great."

The day the great fire—and then the other fire—red—red—all over red. Somebody, somebody, Sara. "Sara—Sara—Sara—Sara."

"What's he yellin', man?"

"I don't know, boy—but go get Miss Riley next door. Doc doesn't want 'em too excited."

"Okay, okay."

"Easy man, take it easy, boy—stop yellin', man, take it easy."

I can do it with ease—with ease Sara—now watch—2 lengths of the pool under water—Sara—2 lengths.

"He seems all right, Sam."

"He was just yellin' a minute ago, Miss Riley."

"Don't forget to tell the doctor—I'll write it down but you remind him."

"Yes, ma'am, I will."

"May be a good sign."

"Sure hope so."

☐☐

"Get a move on, boy, got a lot to do."

"Okay, okay."

Still, I'll stay still—stiller than still—still—still.

"Come on, let's go."

Stay—stay—stay still—still.

"I'm comin'—I'm comin'."

☐☐

"Hello, Frank—it's me, Dr. Green. I'm just going to sit here by your side."

Sit, sit, the empty-voiced emptiness—sitting sitting empty—a shadow—a voiced shadow.

□□

"Sam, would you please put these shades up —leave in some light."

"Yes, sure, Miss Riley."

Running down a dark alley—a narrow dark alley—houses, windows on both sides, shades dark and drawn, drawn and dark. Closed eyes, blind to the runner. A shade up here, a shade up there—light through the windows. Windows that look out like eyes—shades that go up like eyelids. The runner runs blindly on —he sees nothing and can't stop—the window eyes look on and on.

"That's better, Sam—thanks."

"Welcome, Miss Riley."

□□

"Time for a buzz, man—gotta get you ready for yo buzz."

"That's no way to talk, Jack."

"Gee, Sam, you touchy lately or somethin'?"

"Man, I'm not touchy—it's just not right —not right for Frank here or these other guys."

"Not right? Look boy, he can't hear—I mean—look—he pays no attention—none."

"I'm not sure, man—but shut up. Here comes Dr. Finch."

Finch, bull finch—bull, bull—bull—a shower of bull finches—and bull manure—and a kick in the head—the head—the toilet. All right. Jack—I dig you, Jack.

"Everything all set, boys?"

"Yes, doctor."

"Where's Miss Riley?"

"She's off today, doctor."

"Then Miss Smith?"

Smitty, smutty—come let's run—let's run, Smitty, let's run.

"Here she comes."

"Hi, Miss Smith."

"Hello, doctor."

"All right, the tongue depressor—hold on now—here goes."

Going, going, gone.

"Waxy flexibility—no, he hasn't really demonstrated it. Find it in more chronic cases."

"Yet, there is a hell of a stiffness—a stubbornness."

Stiff, stiff—stiff in hell—wax—candles burning in hell. Roman candles—Nero fiddling —Rome burns—candles, rockets to the sky— the fourth of July—remember the fourth— the noise — firecrackers — 2-incher — 3-incher —6-incher—penis 6 inches—it aches—still mine.

"Schizophrenic reaction—catatonic type— acute."

Cute—the baby—how cute.

"Say, better move on—may hear us."

Hear us and fear us and leer at us.

□□

"He's dead—look, isn't breathing at all."

"Keep it down, you'll wake 'em all up."

"Okay. Okay. Better call the doctor."

Dead, dead—me dead. So I am dead—the body is dead—the voices—they say it. Now they know—cold—white coldness—stones— stones—stone cold dead—stone cold dead.

"Where you goin'?"

"Cover Frank over there—cover slipped off him."

Cover dead and covered—away and buried —covered.

"Here, boy, tuck you in—cold in here. Stiff, like dead, boy—but not you, Frankie—alive and kicking."

"What the hell you doin'? Talking to yourself?"

"Talking to Frank over here, boy."

"He can't hear you. Stop shining the damn light in his eyes—get him all excited. Go get the doc—so he can pronounce this guy here."

The bright pearly light in the eyes—the orange, reddish glow. Oh the redness of it. It welled up and up and up. Stiffer and stiffer. Holding tight—and then cool black again. The void—the sinking into the depths of the deep-blue nothingness—for dead is dead and nothing at all.

"It's time for your treatment, Frank."

"Shall I plug it in, doctor?"

"Yes, please do, Miss Smith."

Plug it in and burn. The Books of Knowledge—the little boy—the picture of Joan of Arc at the stake—oh that volume—make sure, pop—make sure, skip it—and sometimes wanting to look—but never looking—never.

"Okay."

☐☐

CAT

"Hello, here I am again, Frank. It's me, Dr. Green."

Green, yellow, blue and white—none of it dark—none of it night.

"Frank, I'll just sit here with you."

Sit, how he sat—and sat and waited and waited and Billy—red and roly and round was born. Is he all there—all Frank—fingers all all right. All there, son, all there—all all right.

He looks like you, Frank, like you and like pop—just like pop and uncle Will.

Pop—pop—and uncle Will—like a death sentence. The doctors, nurses—relatives her—that look—that hopelessness look—the talking in whispers—the death watch before the death —no dignity—no dignity—oh Sara—no dignity. They buried him before he died.

See Frank again going toward the bed—and thinking, No, it couldn't be pop—pop alive and bubbling. The man on the bed—his eyes dull and blind—his mouth half open and sunken—his face fixed as in stone.

□□

"At least this guy gets excited, yells sometimes."

"What do you mean, Sam?"

"Well, at least he's alive sometimes—not like Jake down there."

"Jake, that Jake, that Jake is the living dead."

Jake, Jake the dead, Jake the ripper—Jake electrocuted and dead.

"Gee, Sam, you think this guy will ever start eatin' himself? This here tube feedin'—you think it gives him any nourishment?"

"Look, Jack—what do I know? Me, I'm just an attendant—just like you."

"Yeah, but you been around here a long time, man."

"Well, the treatments sometimes help."

"You mean the shock?"

"Yeah, man, the shock."

"Boy, them treatments ain't pretty."

"Pretty, not pretty—you want 'em to come alive, to start eatin'."

"Ask me, he's eatin' all right—he's eatin' himself up alive."

Eating himself—hands—and arms and legs and belly all disappearing into a big mouth.

"Come on, Jack—we got a lot to do yet."

"Okay man—okay, I'm comin'."

Coming—coming—coming and going and coming.

There is a big rock—the Rock of Gibraltar —stuck in the mud. It doesn't budge. Waves come in, waves go out, waves hit the rock —they hit it again and again. They go in and out, in out, in and out again. The rock is still, is dead, is never moved at all.

"Jesus, look at it rain, boy!"

Rain, no picnic—not this time—next week, Frankie. Don't feel bad, son, don't feel bad.

Bad—next week—next week, pop—next week. But the boy said nothing—only thought it.

The way the rain bends them—almost to the ground.

They'll break, pop—they'll break. No, Frankie—no—the rain is good for them—it's good. You know, son—for things to grow you need days of rain.

"Maybe it'll stop—maybe before we go home."

"Maybe, but, pal, they're sure big drops comin' down."

For things to grow you need them—big drops.

"Take it easy, take it easy. This shot will calm you, make you feel better."

Shot—all right—then, to be shot—electrocuted, shot—burned. This body can't be killed—killed inside—killed and dead—and the flesh, the lumpity, lump, lump of it, quivers and jumps, sees red and lives and waits for the shot to kill and be dead—dead—let it die and be dead—and yet asleep—a sleepy—tired—soft blue sleepiness—creeps into the death—a stirs up some life a sleepy to sleep life.

"That's it, Frank, calm down—easy does it—better now, isn't it?"

It is calmed down and better and tired and drifting on a river this way and that way—this way and that.

"He must have fallen asleep."

"Yes, sort of."

Asleep—sort of—yes.

□□

"Time for your treatment, Frank."

Stiff—stiff.

"Hold him."

"Yes, doctor."

"Got him, Sam?"

"Yes, sir."

Stiff—stiff.

"Give me the tongue depressor."

"Here, sir."

"Come on, Frank—open your mouth—we want to help you, Frank."

"Stubborn—never had this trouble before."

"Not stubborn, Miss Riley. Scared."

Stiff—stiff.

"Come on, Frank — open up — open — please."

"Can we do it without the gag?"

"Break his teeth."

"Careful now."

Stiff—stiff.

"Please, Frank, please—we want to help, not hurt you."

"Can I try, doctor?"

"Sure, Sam."

"Here, Frank boy—open your mouth, fella —here, Frank—thata fella—thanks, boy— you're okay, boy, okay. You gonna be all right, Frank—all right—Dr. Green—and the treatments—okay."

Green—softer and softer and softer.

"I'll be damned—got 'em?"

"Yes."

"Here goes, then."

□□

"Put the lights out."

"Leave the night light?"

"Sure, always leave the night light."

All the lights—Frank—electricity burning up money, Frank—study less—sleep—shoveling—a giant shovel, a steam shovel—shoveling millions and millions of electric bills and dollar bills and all into a bright green bonfire, a special fire that's green and burns only bills and money.

"You off tomorrow?"

"Sure am, pal."

"Gee, be nice if got off weekends like in regular jobs."

"Jack, you're the cryin'est guy I know."

Cryin'—cryin' out loud—cryin' softly—dried up tears to cry no more.

Don't cry, Frank—never cry—boys and men don't cry—it's for girls, boy—remember. Only for girls—you feel like it—never mind—keep it in—lump in your chest? lump in your throat? It'll melt, boy—it'll melt—don't see your mom cry—do you? and I'm a woman—a woman.

She called herself a woman, Sara.

I know, Frank.

"Gee, this place is depressing with the lights out."

"Guess you're eager to go home, man."

"Sure am—I sure am—I'm blowin' this joint."

Blowin' on a joint of beef—beefin'—Frank, there's no use beefin'—when your father died I beefed and beefed and beefed—and then I knew no use beefin'—I went out and worked —no use beefin'.

"How about it, Sam—want some outside food?"

"No, I'm eatin' here."

"I'm gonna buy me some Chinese grub—tired of this hospital chow."

"I don't mind it."

"Okay, Samuello."

Chinese food—the Old China Inn—so many different dishes—the waiter looked at us—just 2—2 people. Just 2—bring it out, all of it—bring it out.

"See you later."

"Okay."

Okay, okay and he brought it out—wanton soup.

Soup—through tubes—into stomachs—disconnected from the talkless mouths.

"Will he come out of it, Dr. Green—will Frank here be all right?"

"I hope so—but it's up to Frank—it has a lot to do with him."

"Doc, does he hear us? You talk like he hears us."

"I don't know, Sam—but I think Frank hears us. I think he does."

"His eyes are—"

"I know, but he can hear."

Hear, smear—hope—out of it—voices, voices out of it—into it. Drifting along—on a blue sea—shimmering on the surface of a million glass eyeballs. Glass eyeballs. My eyes—my eyes—mine—still mine—my eyes—

"Doc. He hears us—he hears us—look, look how he quick, sudden-like—moved his hands to his eyes!"

"Yes, Frank, you can hold your eyes, hold them if you like. I'll sit here and wait. I'll wait till you're ready."

"So long, doc."

"See you later, Sam."

Later, later—hold my eyes—and sit and wait. I'll hold them and wait for later.

□ □

Hear it—the rain—cats and dogs—dogs, the twirling dog. Twirling dog—twirling, twirling, twirling—see the white poodle. It lies on its back. The man twirls it about faster, faster, still faster. Then the man picks it up and puts it on its feet. The dog's head goes up and back dizzily. It can hardly stand on its feet. The man laughs and says, Did you ever—did you ever, Frankie—did you ever see such a silly mutt. Mutt—mud—mud. There is the surf again. The sand is muddy. There is the man again. He hangs from a cloud. He is carving the dog up now with a long knife. Blood drips down, turning the sand into red mud. Red, red, but this time Frank is ready. He holds the redness down. He doesn't let it come. He keeps things blue—cool and blue—blue and cool. The voice breaks in. "It's time for your supper, Frank. You gotta eat, man. Man, you gotta eat." He hears the liquid splash through the tube. "Man, you gotta get strong—you gotta get to yoself again."

Man, he thought, man—he Frank—somebody, man—strong, self.

□ □

He heard them. He heard their voices. He understood what their voices said. It was as if that stubborn lump that was in him and controlled him melted a little bit.

"Frank, we have to do it. We have to get this new tube into your stomach. We are going to push it through your nose into your stomach. Don't be afraid, Frank. This will be a little uncomfortable, but we won't hurt you."

The other voice said, "He doesn't know a word you're saying."

He wasn't afraid. They finally understood. They were going to replace some of the life that had leaked out the other tube—the tube in the penis, the penis—his penis—was it still his? He didn't know. He couldn't feel it.

He heard them pour the milky substance into the tube in his nose. It was life. It felt like life. He felt a feeling, now a tingle, a something, a little less frozen. Maybe his penis was still his. He heard them talk. "If this guy would only eat—wouldn't have to bother with this damned Levine tube feeding. God, that catheter has been in him for days. If he'd only start to piss—take the damned thing out. Amazing —didn't gag on the tube a bit. Dead as a doormat."

"Say, take it easy. He can hear us, you know.

"Hear me. You crazy. Guy lies here with his mouth open, stiff as a board."

"I tell you these catatonics register everything. Not only hear it all, but remember it too."

The voices stopped.

☐☐

Frank hears, but does it register? He is much too busy concentrating on the sensation in his penis. The life in his belly must have gone to his penis. But it is no use. It is leaking out again. It is leaking out of the tube sticking in him.

He is there. Frank knows he is there. Frank knows it. His shadow moves across Frank's eyes when he moves. Frank doesn't move. The stubbornness—it is hard—hard and all over —spread—spread all over like a cancer—like a fire—red—oh the red—the red redable red —red it.

He started to twist and turn and thrash about.

"You're irritated, Frank—am I annoying you? Are you annoyed—angry? I don't expect an answer, Frank. I'll talk from time to time. You hear me, Frank. But you don't have to answer, I'll still be here."

Annoyed. Annoyed—angry—oh the redness, the redness of it—green—green—green.

He lies still and falls asleep—sleeping for the first time in a long time.

Sleeping, waking, sleeping, waking.

Yes, the shadow is there—it is there—the shadow. But the voice is gone for now. The ghosted voice speaks not.

□□

It is silent now—the silent, dead world of the moon. Snowflakes falling on endless water —landwater, that doesn't move—dead water and the flakes disappearing and this deadness me, the deadest of all in the middle of it all. Not a sound. Hear, hear, a voice—but it won't, it can't come in—the silence of the silent muffles it out—safe in silence—silence in safety.

"Hello, Frank. I'm sitting with you, Frank." A screech, a little tire screech—screeching its way into the silence. Out—out—ha, ha, out, out.

"Hello, doc. I washed him up nice and clean."

"Thanks, Sam. He looks much better."

"You just gonna sit with him, doc?"

"I sure am, Sam. I'm going to sit here with Frank, and if he wants to talk—well, we'll talk."

The tire screeching louder. The snow gone, the silent world broken. The voices chopping it up into a loudness—tire screechings that say words like Frank wants.

□□

"I'm here, Frank, Dr. Green."

Green slime—never liked lime—give me orange and yellow—not red—not red—cool blue cool cool.

"I'll sit here for our hour."

Our, our, arf, arf—throwing pillows at barking dogs.

"It's sure cold."

Frozen stiff—a stiff cadaver—

"Cold out today, Frank. Thought I'd never thaw out."

Rotting sores do thaw, a green cadaver—rotting in the sun—

"I won't say anything more, Frank—I'll just sit."

The dog is silent, won't have a fit.

Whitie and Brownie and Lucky and Skippy and the tortoise, and the goldfish and the guppy, and where are they now?

Running along the water's edge all together —a bright sun—a bright son. You have a bright son, Mr., Mr., Mrs.—he should go far, far. Far, that's a laugh—oh, he's smart, all right —but school means money—and his father's gone far—far, far away.

□□

"Dr. Green, I thought this guy never moved."

"What do you mean?"

"Well, this morning he had his hands at his sides—now they're back to his eyes again."

"Yes, I see."

See—I see you there—you lump of voices settled there—on chairs, shaking and quaking —this way and that—2 voices—squeaking and sharp, a skinny voice; deep and round, a fat voice.

"Guess Frank feels like holding his hands up now."

Feels—a lump feels—feels a lump.

"You sure have patience, doc."

Patients, a doctor has patients—many, many —little nobody patients—each patient a no-body—no body—but eyes—hold them—not to melt and let them drip out.

"So long, doc."

"So long, Sam."

Uncle Sam's cabin.

□□

"You had a treatment, Frank. Dr. Finch gave you a treatment. I'm here as I promised to be when you woke up. If you're tired, close your eyes—sleep. I'll sit here with you."

Sit—sit—sit—his body ached—it ached all over—he was tired. But he felt his muscles— loose, but he felt them. He felt—and he felt tired. Felt—fell—asleep—a black soothing void—away from the shadowed voice.

Back to the fish—the dried-up fish—the day the goldfish jumped out of the bowl—and Whitey got killed in the car, and pop. Oh, the dried-up fish. He put it in the bowl. He poked it around. It got softer, but wouldn't swim. Mom—no lunch. She threw the goldfish into the toilet.

He opened his eyes and licked his lip. He felt very dry—dried out. The shadow put the glass to his mouth. He sipped a little water.

"Good morning, Frank. I'm going to sit on this chair near your chair, Frank. I'm glad to see that they've sat you up."

Sit on a chair. A chair whose legs are claws that tear into the ground, clutch clutching it, claws that clutch. The chair and me—one and the same—clutching the ground like an embedded rock.

"Hello, doc."

"Hi, Sam."

"Do you want to be alone with him?"

"Yes—Sam—I want to sit—just with Frank here."

Just Frank—just Frank—there is no justice, justice for Frank—chained to the floor by a clawed chair—clutching a piece of ground in each claw. The ground is dry and hard—where is the ocean? Where is the sand? Where is the vastness—the lovely land? Voices here, voices there—voices on the ground and on the chair.

"Okay, see you later, Dr. Green."

"So long, fella."

Fella, yella—green slime—never liked lime. Not with a dime—10 cents—10 cents for a hot dog on the boardwalk—there it is again on a cold winter day—the ghost town—the long, empty boardwalk stretching off along the line of the seashore—lovely, quiet, unafraid.

"It's a nice day, Frank."

How do you know? You're not part of the show—the empty boardwalk is empty—the freak show—a big sign—come and see—free, free, see Dr. Green's freaks—the walking, lying, reclining, sitting dead.

"Good morning, Frank, I'm here for our hour."

Frank, I think you're a no-good SOB.

Why, Mahoney, why?

"It's a lovely day today, Frank."

I'm gonna rip the card, Frank.

Don't do it, Mahoney, don't do it.

"You seem to be annoyed."

Can't take it, can you, Frank?

Leave me alone, Mahoney, get out—I can't stand your voice—leave me, leave me.

"I'll just sit, Frank, I'll just be here."

You're gone, Mahoney—gone—your voice is gone. Scoot—scoot—you've scooted off.

The day he brought the scooter—it was at night. Going to sleep night after night—waking—the mornings always the same—school. But that morning—wake up—wake up, Frank, school. Okay, pop, and there—against the wall —the bright yellow scooter—with a brake —balloon tires—pop, pop. You like it, Frank? Pop. After school on the boardwalk—lucky —lucky balloon tires—doesn't go between the boards. Polishing and polishing—how it shone.

"Our hour is over, Frank. See you later—so long."

CAT

Mahoney, it's mine—it's mine—my father, he bought it for me—it's called Indian Racer—
Who ever heard of a scooter with a name? It's Indian Racer!
Your voice is gone again, Mahoney—raced —raced away.

☐☐

"It's sure a gray day out, Miss Riley."

"Yes, one day spring is in the air, the next day feels like snow."

Gray days and green days—and green's voice—Green and his voice—green—a green man's voice—green grass and flowers—and spring. The magnolia tree blossoming for a week and then the blossoms are gone—for a whole year.

"Hello, Frank. It's me again—here to sit with you."

Here to sit—Green on a gray, gray day, here to sit.

□□

"Here are some flowers, Frank—there's a card from the school. Dr. Green said to put them near your bed. Maybe you can smell them—they're nice—really beautiful, Frank —really beautiful—real nice—a big mixed bunch."

Flowers—flowers for my grave. When I'm dead—when I'm dead—roses.

"They must like you, boy—they wish you the best."

Green juice—green blood—through stems to leaves. But, the tips dead—rotten.

"See you later, boy."

□□

"Gee, Miss Riley, how many does this make?"

"A dozen, Sam. Just a dozen."

"A dozen ECT's. I thought—well, it seemed like more."

A dozen roses.

"Hello, folks."

"Hello, doctor."

"Good morning, Dr. Finch."

"Good morning, sir."

"This makes the twelfth."

A dozen roses—light-yellow roses—

"That a boy—now hold him."

Roses—

PART III

"Frank, Frank, Frank, Frank—hear me, hear me, do you hear me, Frank, Frank, Frank, Frank, Frank, listen, hear me, Frank, Frank, Frank, Frank."

He hears the voice but can't answer. It is as if a stubbornness stands in the way. He wants his mouth to answer, to say it, to say, "I'm Frank, yes, Frank is me, I'm Frank." But the ball of stubbornness sticks firmly in his throat. He can't answer. And yet, a sound— his mouth had made a sound—it said more than a sound—"yes"—it said, "yes."

"Good, Frank, good."

□ □

He could see it on the wall. It was like a movie picture. It was happening again just like it did so long ago. There was a little boy running to the school bus. Just as he got to the door, he heard the big boy speak to the driver. Wait, there's another person coming. Another person; he looked around. There was no other person. Then he realized it was he— he himself—he Frank—he was the other person—he Frank a person. The little boy got on the bus and sat down near the older boy. He felt just a little bit bigger, and was a person.

The voice had a pleasant sound. He touched his face and could feel the lumps and bumps of scar tissue. Then he opened his eyes—and remembered. The fire. His eyes weren't his anymore. They were gone—gone forever—ever—never to see. But the voice. He liked the voice. He, Frank, liked something, somebody, and from the voice he could see, he could see. It was a nice face. He actually liked a face again. "Hello," he said. "Hello, my name isn't Cat, it's Frank."

NOTES

Frank has gone through 3 phases:

1. The first was an autistic phase during which he was often, but not always, oblivious to stimuli around him, even though he heard whatever sounds are described in this book. This phase was marked by much resurgence of earlier memories—a reliving, though sometimes a distorted reliving, of many past events, some of them extremely painful. Time also became distorted—the past, present and future were easily interchangeable, confused and at times melded together. Seconds are sometimes hours and days, and at times days become seconds. There was an abundance of bizarre formulations, symbols of strong unconscious forces.

2. Auditory hallucinations, an early attempt at restitution, ushered in the second phase. During this phase Frank demonstrated increased response to outside stimuli. His response, however, was a unique one. He associated to outside stimuli with his own memories and productions, incorporating them into his own au-

tistic world and communicating none of it outside himself. These responses, for the most part, are divided into 3 groups:

a) the production of associations which sound like the stimuli (a clang-like phenomenon);

b) the production of association responses to the meaning of the stimuli;

c) an emotional response to the emotional content of the stimuli.

Bizarre productions and memories continue in this phase, but are not as prevalent as in phase 1. Toward the end of this phase, he began to be increasingly aware of Dr. Green's presence. This awareness is followed by anger (e.g., "Green—slime—never liked lime") which is the forerunner of a beginning of his acceptance of Dr. Green.

3. He has just initiated the third phase—a response to the outside world and communication with it. Examination, reevaluation and reconstruction may ensue.

The great masterpieces of fantasy by

J. R. R. TOLKIEN

The Hobbit

and

The Lord of the Rings

Part I—THE FELLOWSHIP OF THE RING

Part II—THE TWO TOWERS

Part III—THE RETURN OF THE KING

plus
The Tolkien Reader

It's Wild . . .

It's "Strangelove"

It's Kinky . . .

Better Dead Than Red

a novel by

Stanley Reynolds

The adventures of Franklin Lear (former druggist of Milltown Junction, Vt.) in his crusade against Communist Conspiracy abroad and Creeping Socialism at home.

> *"A wild, hard book, full of ideas—a superbly stylized grotesque, really savage and really funny."*
> —*Michael Frayn of* The Observer